TRAVIS
THE INVISIBL

CW00341014

This publication is not authorised for
sale in the United States of America
and/or Canada.

Sony Music Publishing

Exclusive distributors:
Music Sales Limited, 8/9 Frith Street, London W1D 3JB, England.
Music Sales Pty Limited, 120 Rothschild Avenue, Rosebery, NSW 2018, Australia.

Order No. AM971707
ISBN 0-7119-9042-5
This book © Copyright 2001 by Sony Music Publishing.

Music arranged by Matt Cowe.
Music processed by Paul Ewers Music Design.

Printed in the United Kingdom by
Caligraving Limited, Thetford, Norfolk.

Your Guarantee of Quality:
As publishers, we strive to produce every book to the highest commercial standards.
The music has been freshly engraved and, whilst endeavouring to retain the original running order
of the recorded album, the book has been carefully designed to minimise awkward page turns and
to make playing from it a real pleasure. Particular care has been given to specifying acid-free,
neutral-sized paper made from pulps which have not been elemental chlorine bleached. This pulp
is from farmed sustainable forests and was produced with special regard for the environment.
Throughout, the printing and binding have been planned to ensure a sturdy, attractive publication
which should give years of enjoyment. If your copy fails to meet our high standards, please inform
us and we will gladly replace it.

Music Sales' complete catalogue describes thousands of titles and is available in full colour sections
by subject, direct from Music Sales Limited. Please state your areas of interest and send a cheque/
postal order for £1.50 for postage to: Music Sales Limited, Newmarket Road, Bury St. Edmunds,
Suffolk IP33 3YB.

www.musicsales.com

Guitar Tablature Explained

Guitar music can be notated three different ways: on a musical stave, in tablature, and in rhythm slashes

RHYTHM SLASHES are written above the stave. Strum chords in the rhythm indicated. Round noteheads indicate single notes.

THE MUSICAL STAVE shows pitches and rhythms and is divided by lines into bars. Pitches are named after the first seven letters of the alphabet.

TABLATURE graphically represents the guitar fingerboard. Each horizontal line represents a string, and each number represents a fret.

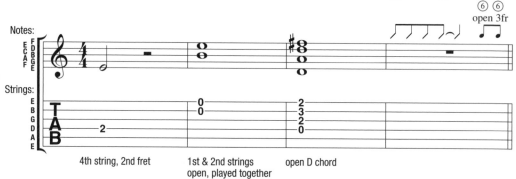

4th string, 2nd fret

1st & 2nd strings open, played together

open D chord

definitions for special guitar notation

SEMI-TONE BEND: Strike the note and bend up a semi-tone (1/2 step).

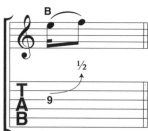

WHOLE-TONE BEND: Strike the note and bend up a whole-tone (whole step).

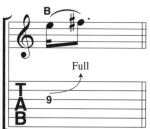

GRACE NOTE BEND: Strike the note and bend as indicated. Play the first note as quickly as possible.

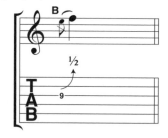

QUARTER-TONE BEND: Strike the note and bend up a 1/4 step.

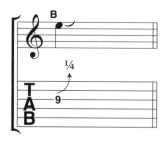

BEND & RELEASE: Strike the note and bend up as indicated, then release back to the original note.

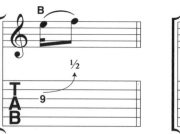

BEND & RESTRIKE: Strike the note and bend as indicated then restrike the string where the symbol occurs.

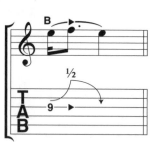

PRE-BEND: Bend the note as indicated, then strike it.

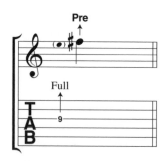

PRE-BEND & RELEASE: Bend the note as indicated. Strike it and release the note back to the original pitch.

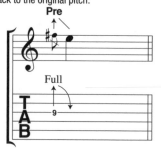

HAMMER-ON: Strike the first (lower) note with one finger, then sound the higher note (on the same string) with another finger by fretting it without picking.

PULL-OFF: Place both fingers on the notes to be sounded. Strike the first note and without picking, pull the finger off to sound the second (lower) note.

LEGATO SLIDE (GLISS): Strike the first note and then slide the same fret-hand finger up or down to the second note. The second note is not struck.

SHIFT SLIDE (GLISS & RESTRIKE): Same as legato slide, except the second note is struck.

NATURAL HARMONIC: Strike the note while the fret-hand lightly touches the string directly over the fret indicated.

PICK SCRAPE: The edge of the pick is rubbed down (or up) the string, producing a scratchy sound.

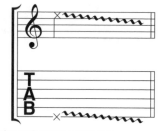

PALM MUTING: The note is partially muted by the pick hand lightly touching the string(s) just before the bridge.

MUFFLED STRINGS: A percussive sound is produced by laying the fret hand across the string(s) without depressing, and striking them with the pick hand.

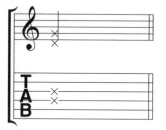

NOTE: The speed of any bend is indicated by the music notation and tempo.

Sing

Words & Music by Fran Healy

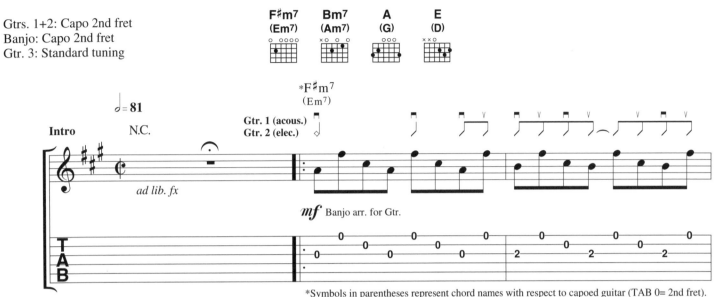

Gtrs. 1+2: Capo 2nd fret
Banjo: Capo 2nd fret
Gtr. 3: Standard tuning

*Symbols in parentheses represent chord names with respect to capoed guitar (TAB 0= 2nd fret).
Symbols above represent actual sounding chords.

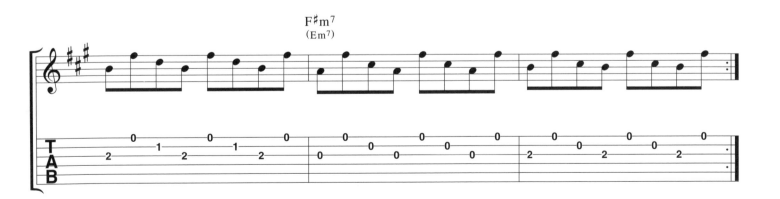

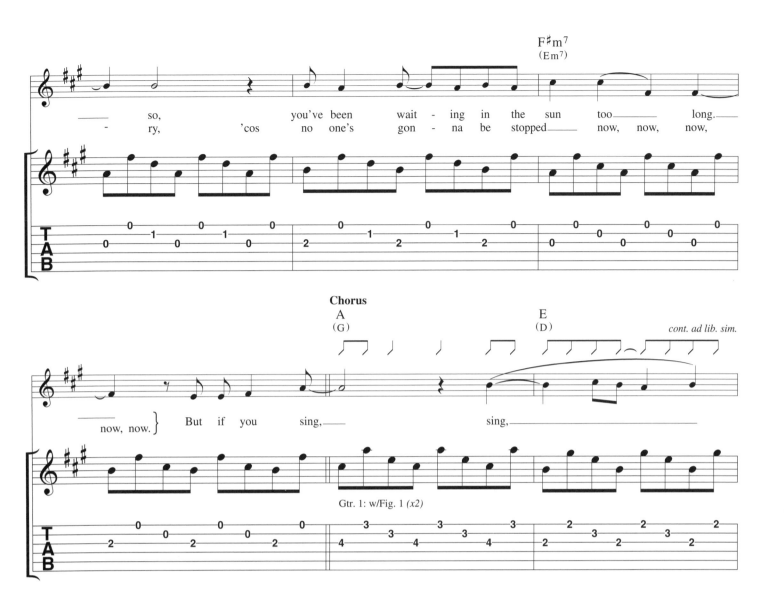

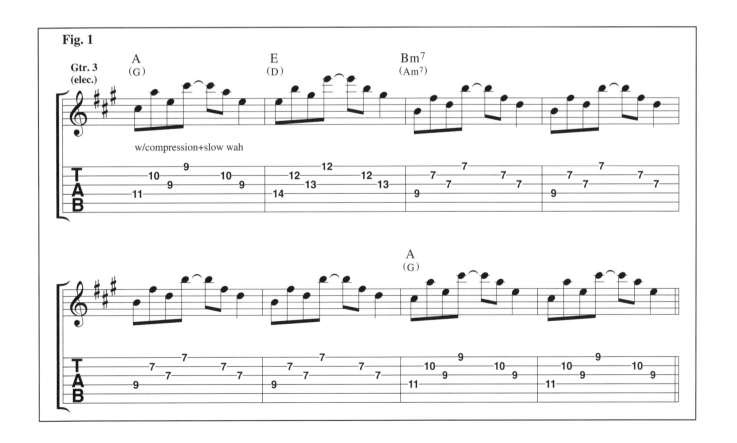

Fig. 1

9

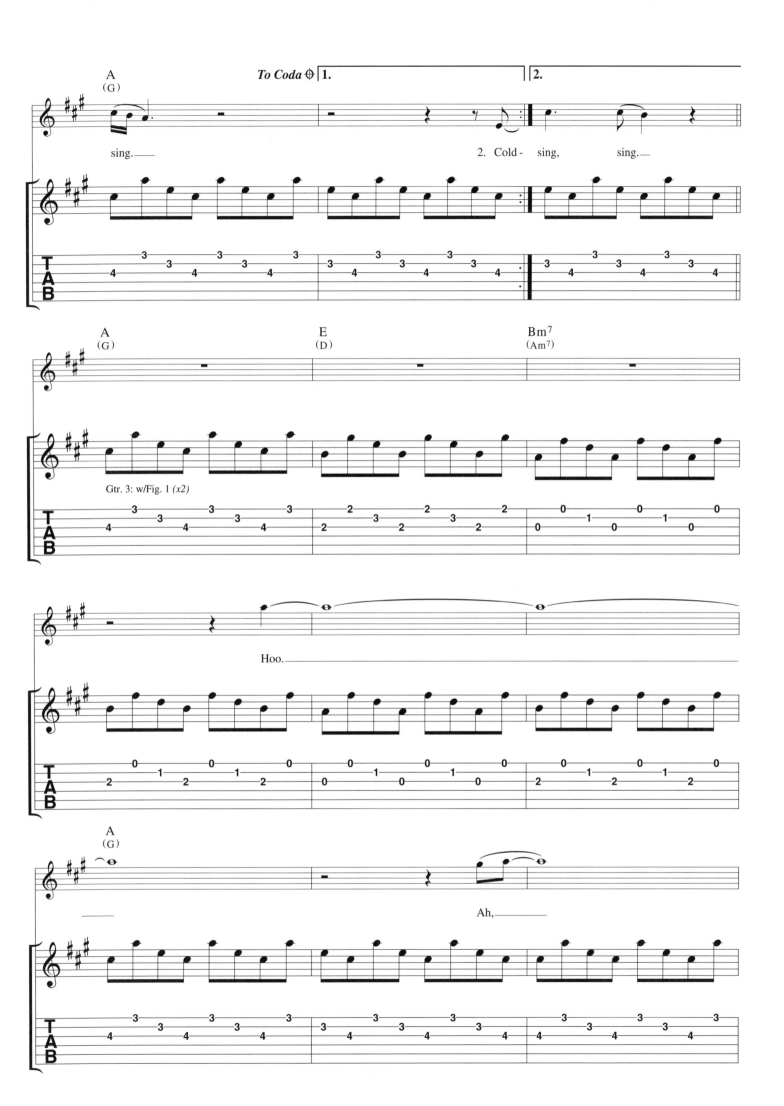

Verse 3:
Baby, there's something going on today
But I say nothing, nothing *(ad lib.)*
So now, now, now, now, now, but if you sing *etc.*

Dear Diary

Words & Music by Fran Healy

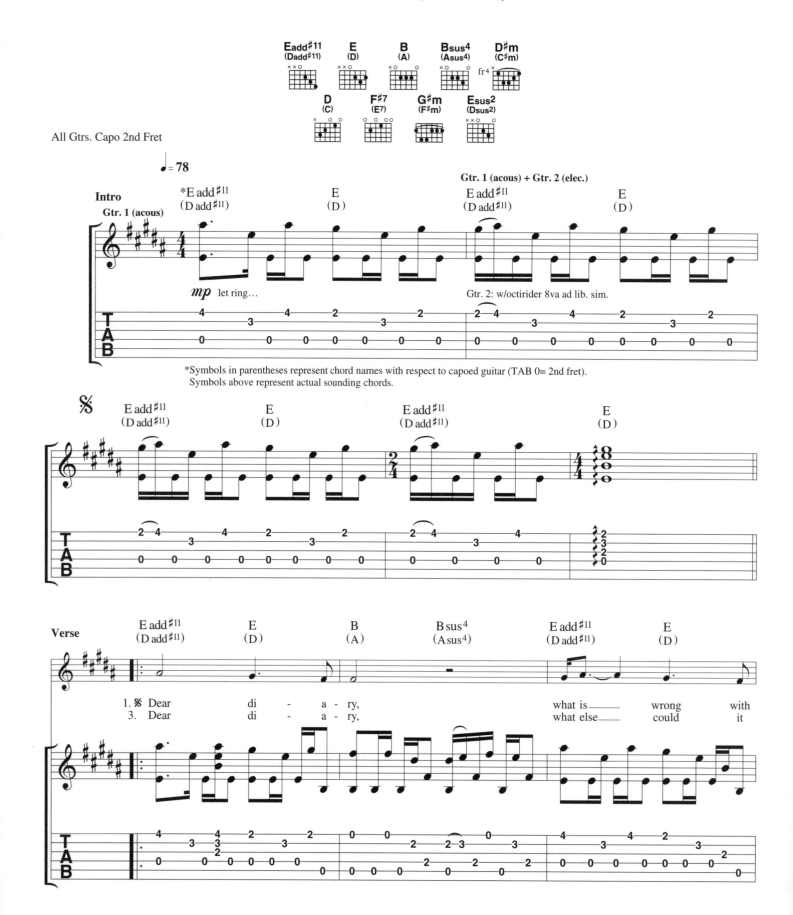

Side

Words & Music by Fran Healy

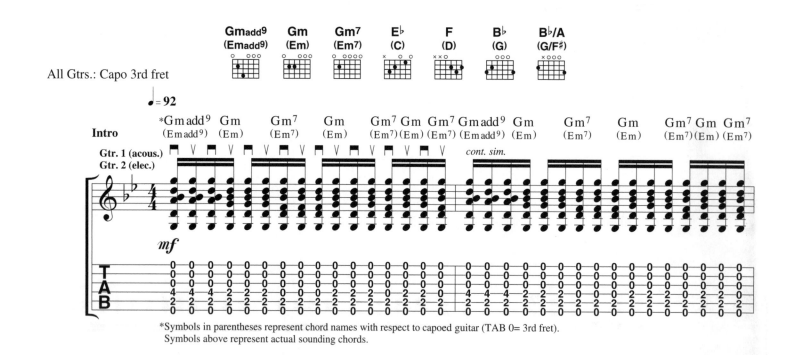

*Symbols in parentheses represent chord names with respect to capoed guitar (TAB 0= 3rd fret).
Symbols above represent actual sounding chords.

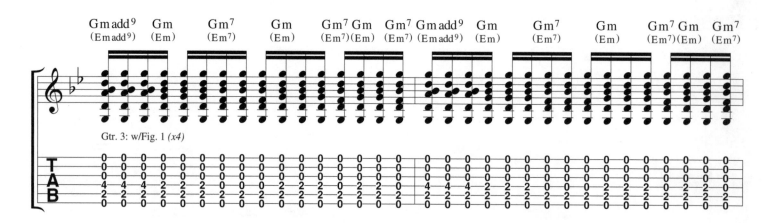

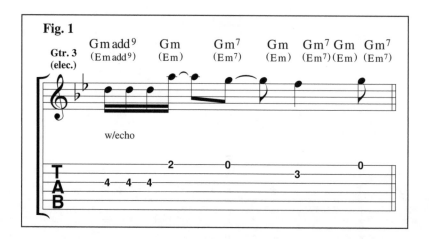

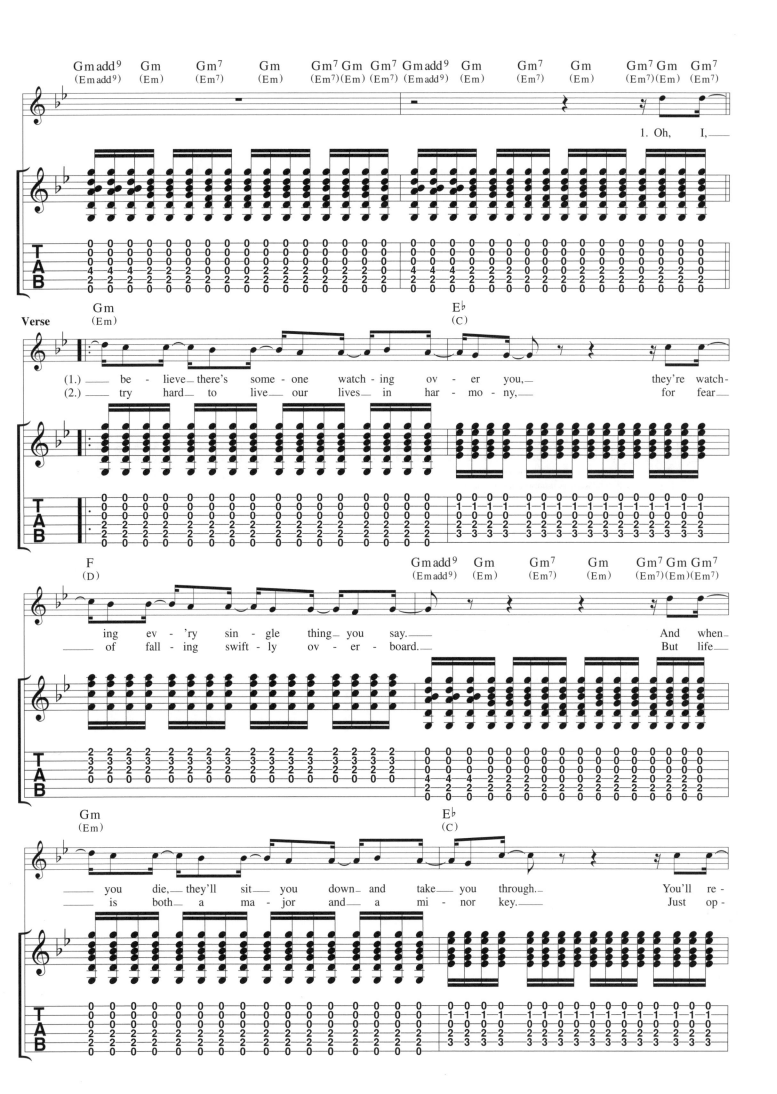

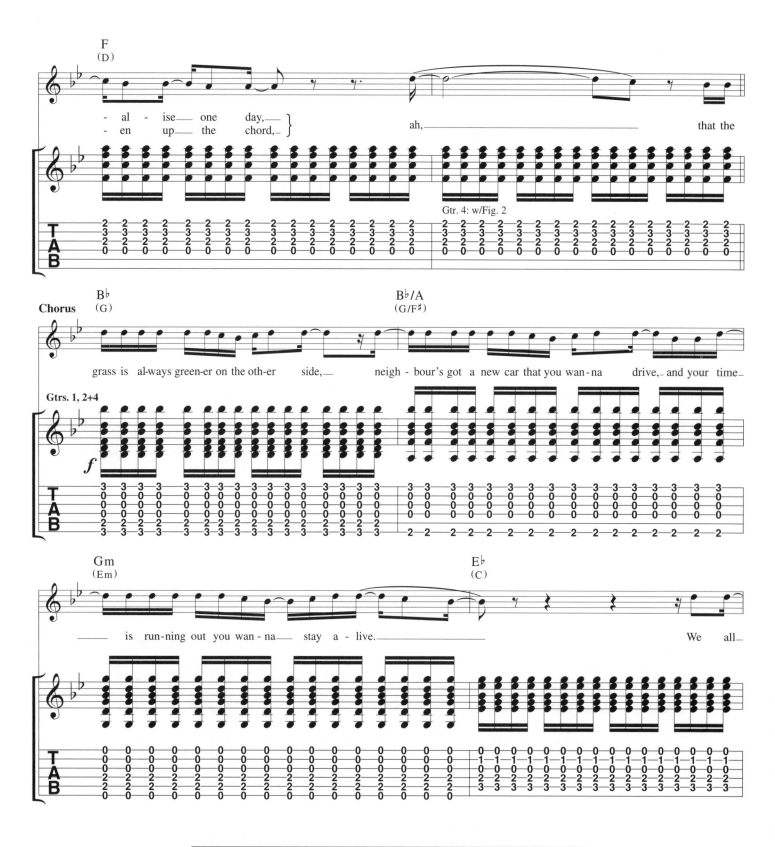

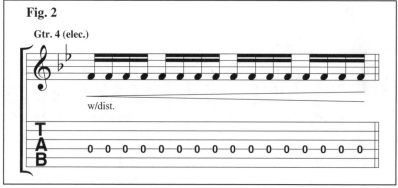

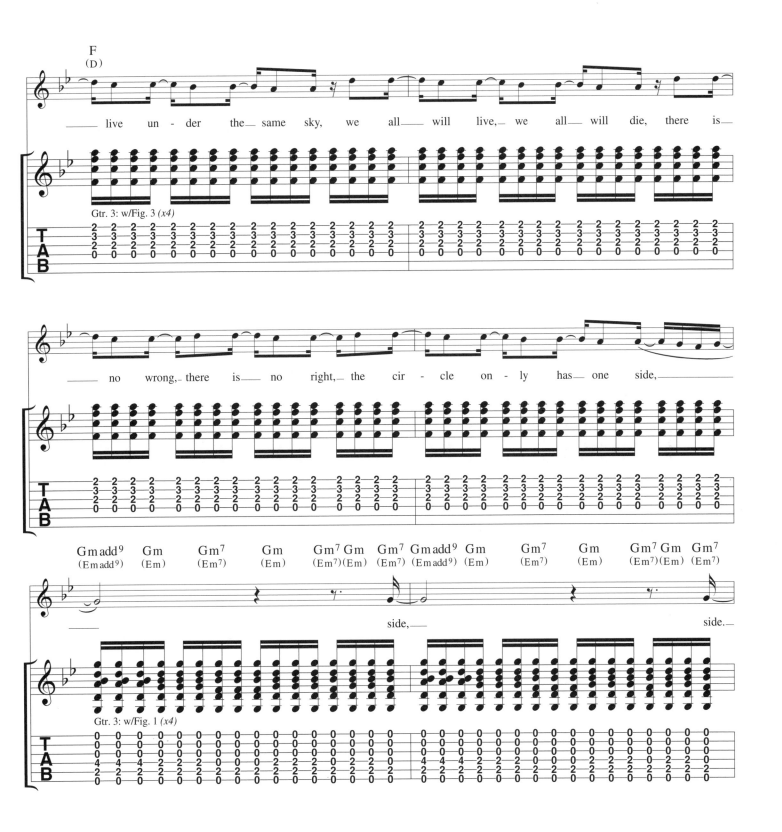

live un-der the same sky, we all will live, we all will die, there is

no wrong, there is no right, the cir-cle on-ly has one side,

Gmadd9 Gm Gm7 Gm Gm7 Gm Gm7 Gmadd9 Gm Gm7 Gm Gm7 Gm Gm7
(Emadd9) (Em) (Em7) (Em) (Em7)(Em) (Em7) (Emadd9) (Em) (Em7) (Em) (Em7)(Em) (Em7)

side, side.

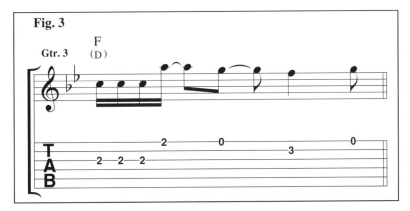

Fig. 3

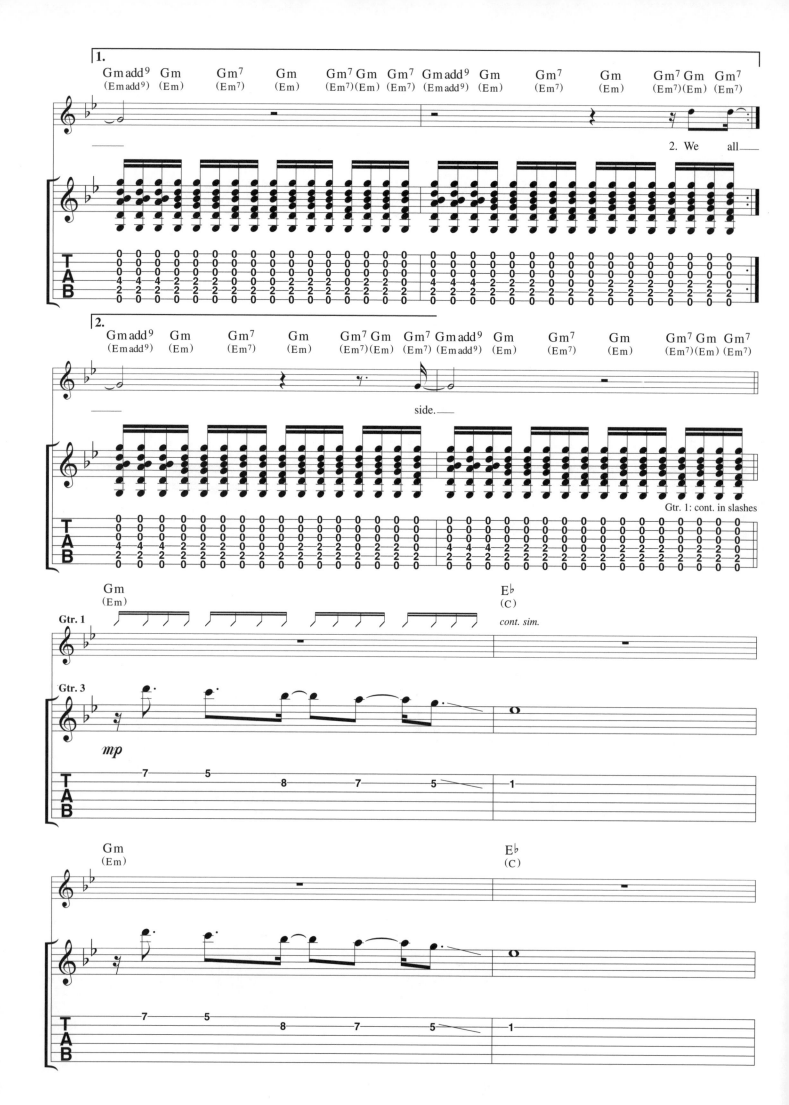

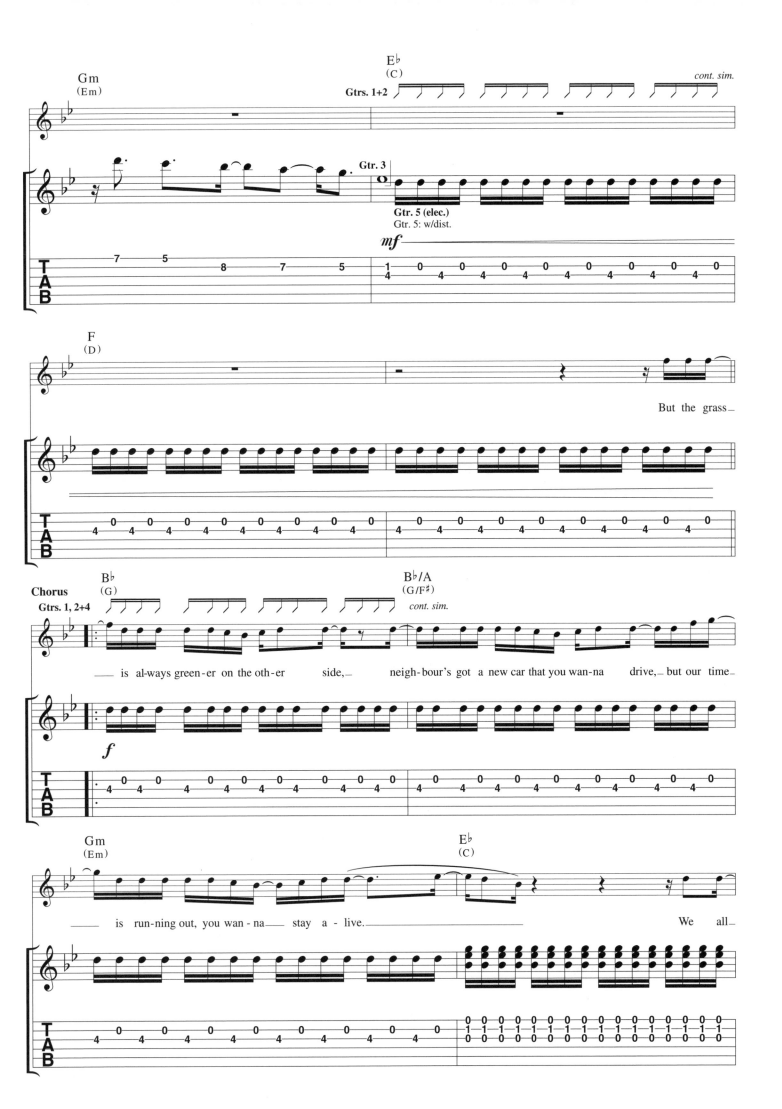

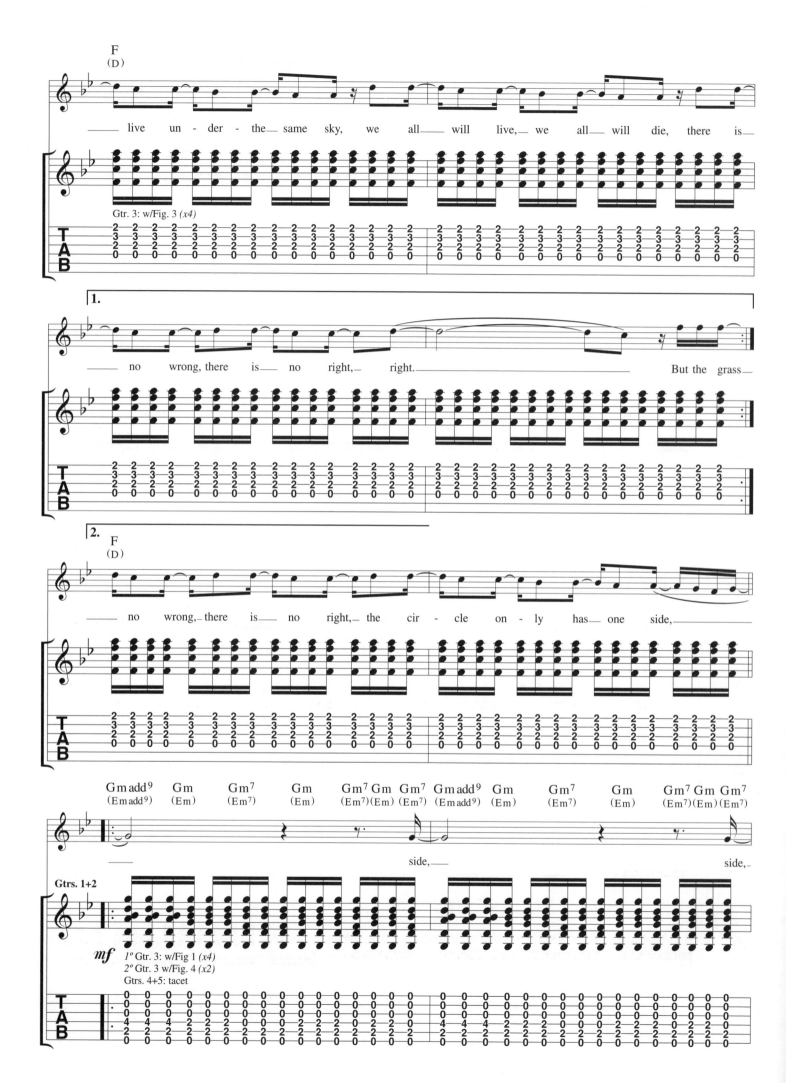

24

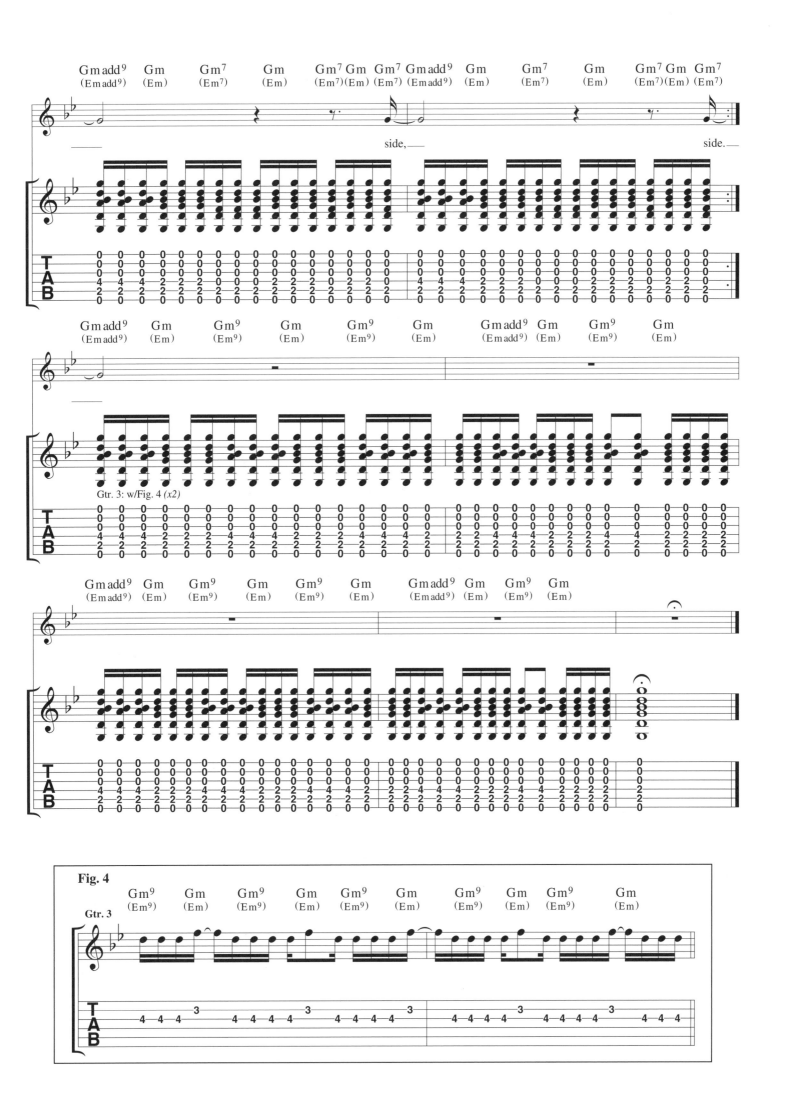

Pipe Dreams

Words & Music by Fran Healy

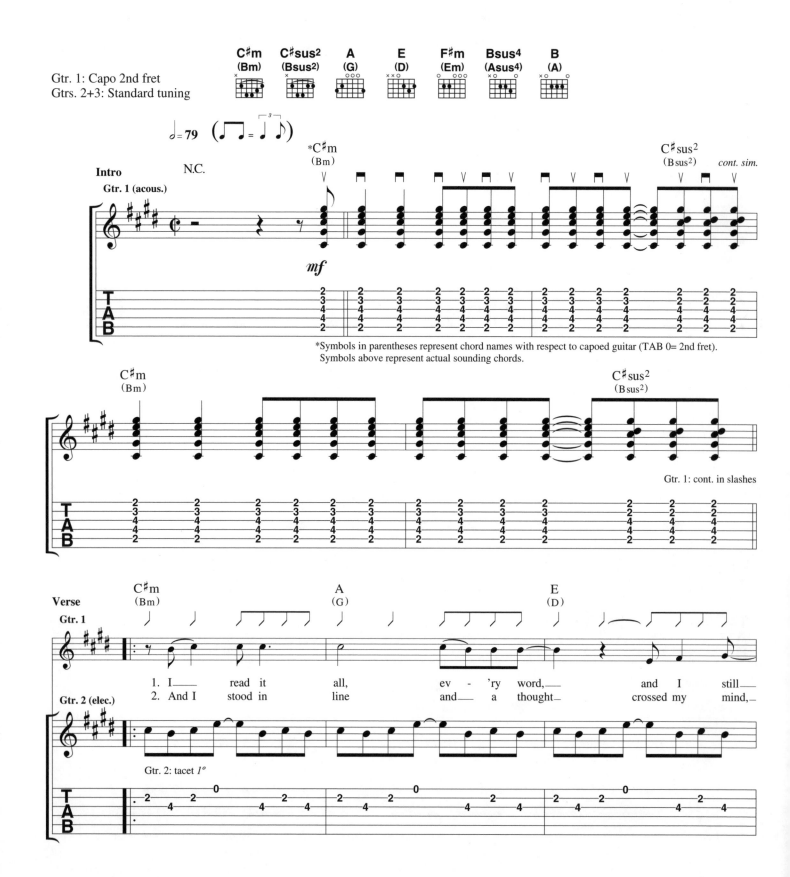

*Symbols in parentheses represent chord names with respect to capoed guitar (TAB 0= 2nd fret).
Symbols above represent actual sounding chords.

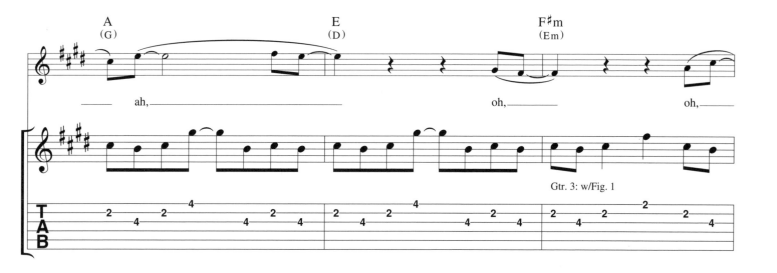

D.%. al Coda

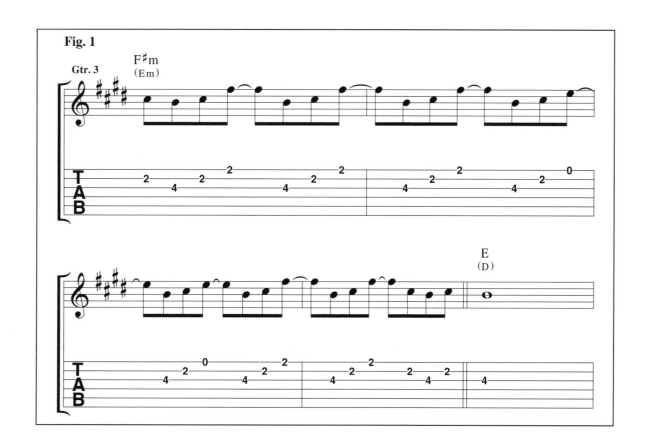

Flowers In The Window

Words & Music by Fran Healy

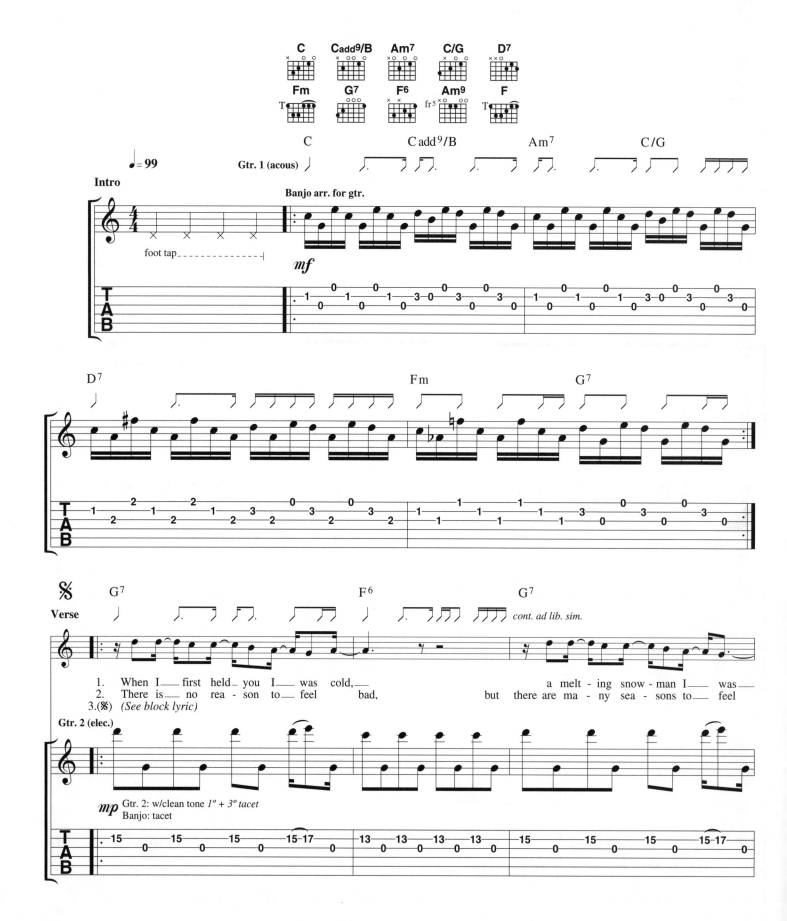

Verse 3:
So now we're here and now is fine
So far away from there and there is time, time, time
To plant new seeds and watch them grow
So there'll be flowers in the window when we go.

Wow, look at us now *etc.*

The Cage

Words & Music by Fran Healy

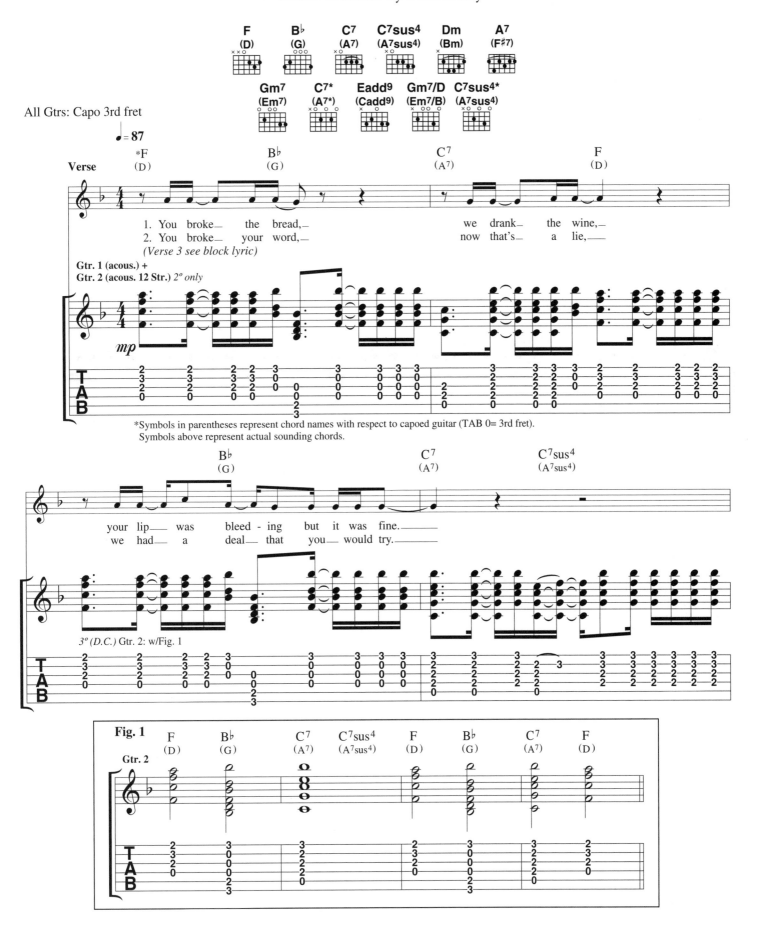

1. You broke— the bread,— we drank— the wine,—
2. You broke— your word,— now that's— a lie,—
(Verse 3 see block lyric)

your lip— was bleed - ing but it was fine.—
we had— a deal— that you— would try.—

*Symbols in parentheses represent chord names with respect to capoed guitar (TAB 0= 3rd fret).
Symbols above represent actual sounding chords.

Fig. 1

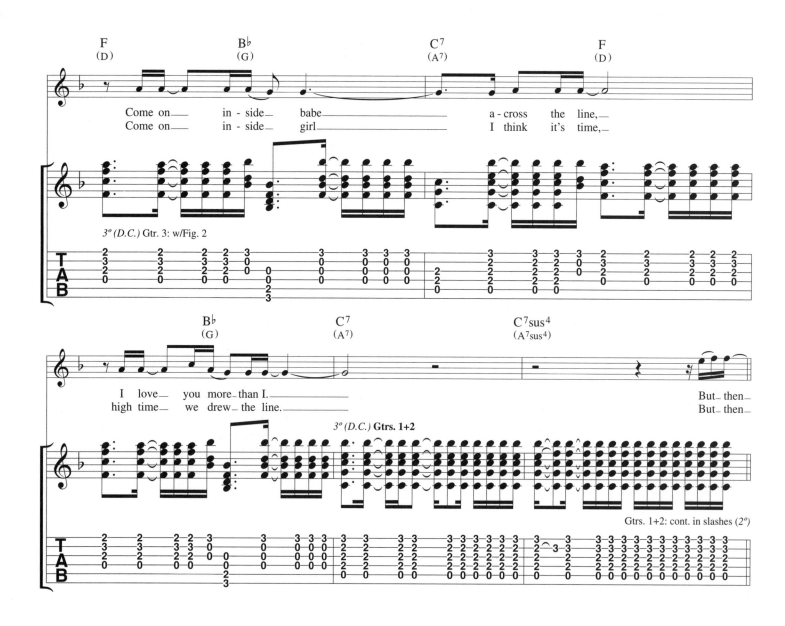

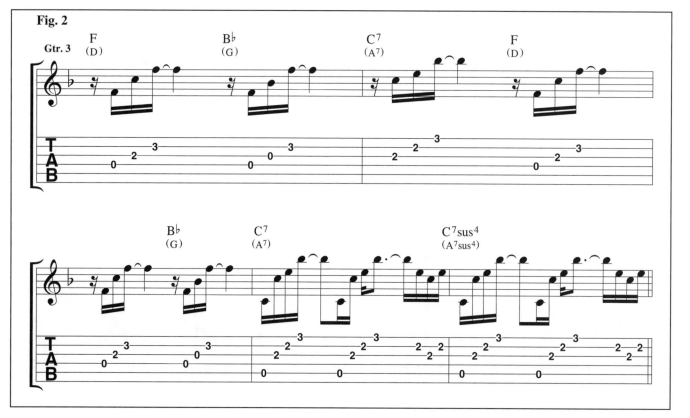

Fig. 2

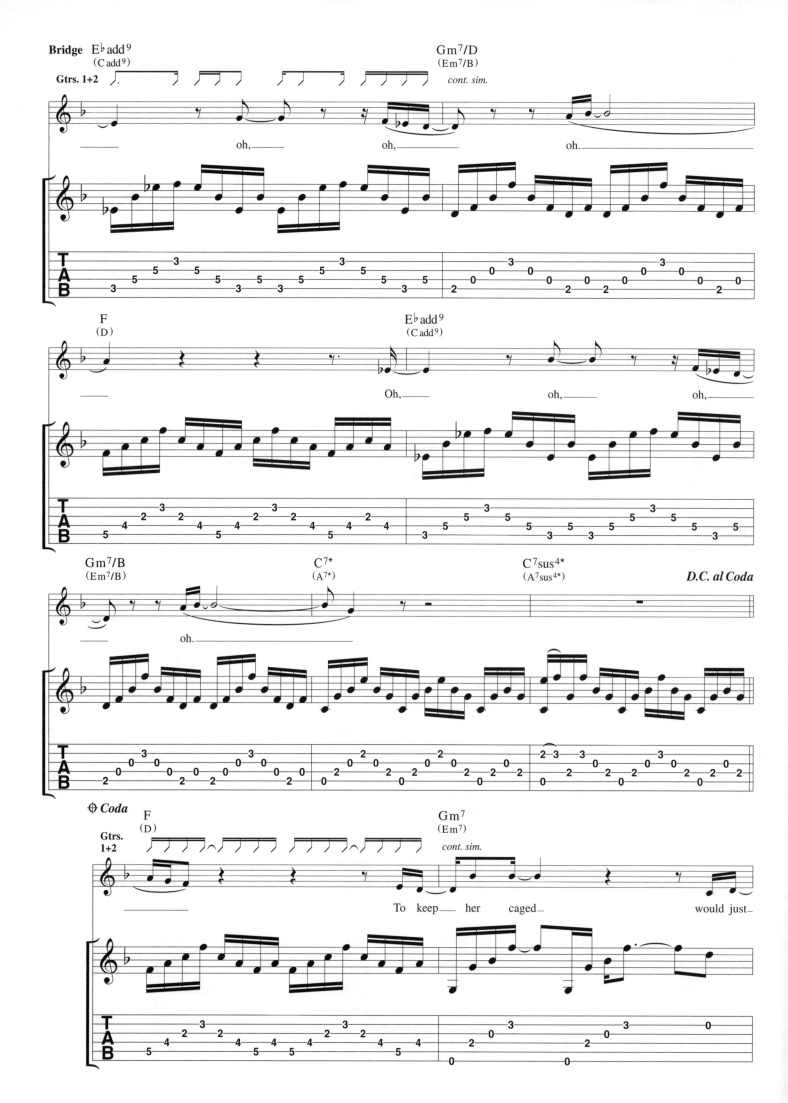

Verse 3:
You broke my soul dear
You stole the plot
You left an empty shot
But there's nothing left here
'Cos you took the lot
An empty cage is all I've got.

'Cos when your bird has flown away
She was never meant to stay
Oh to keep her caged
Would just delay the Spring.

Safe

Words & Music by Fran Healy

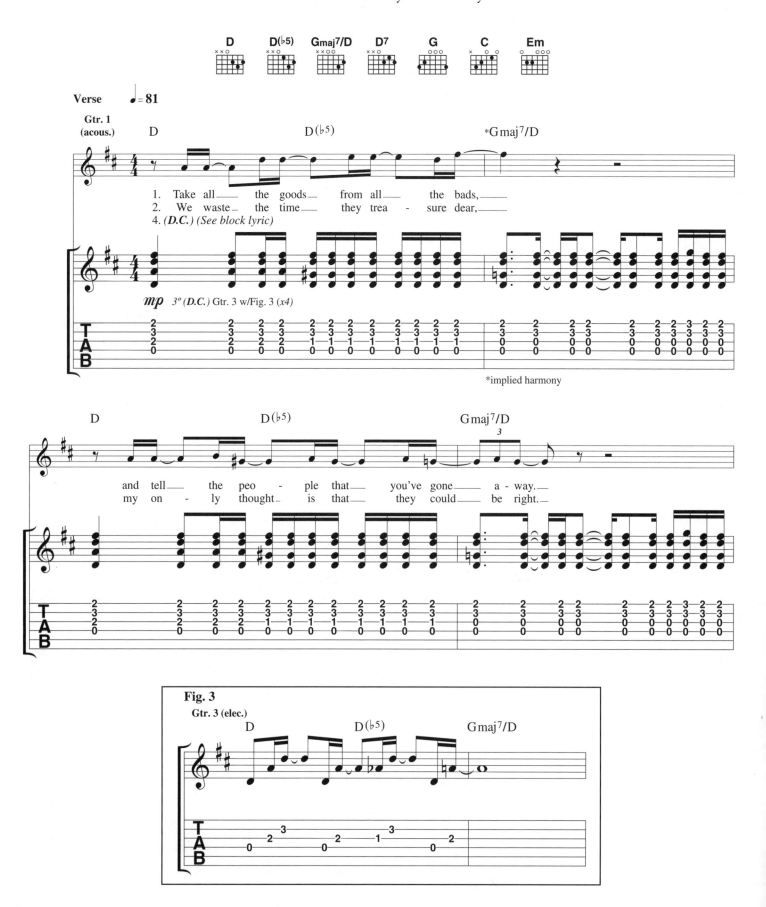

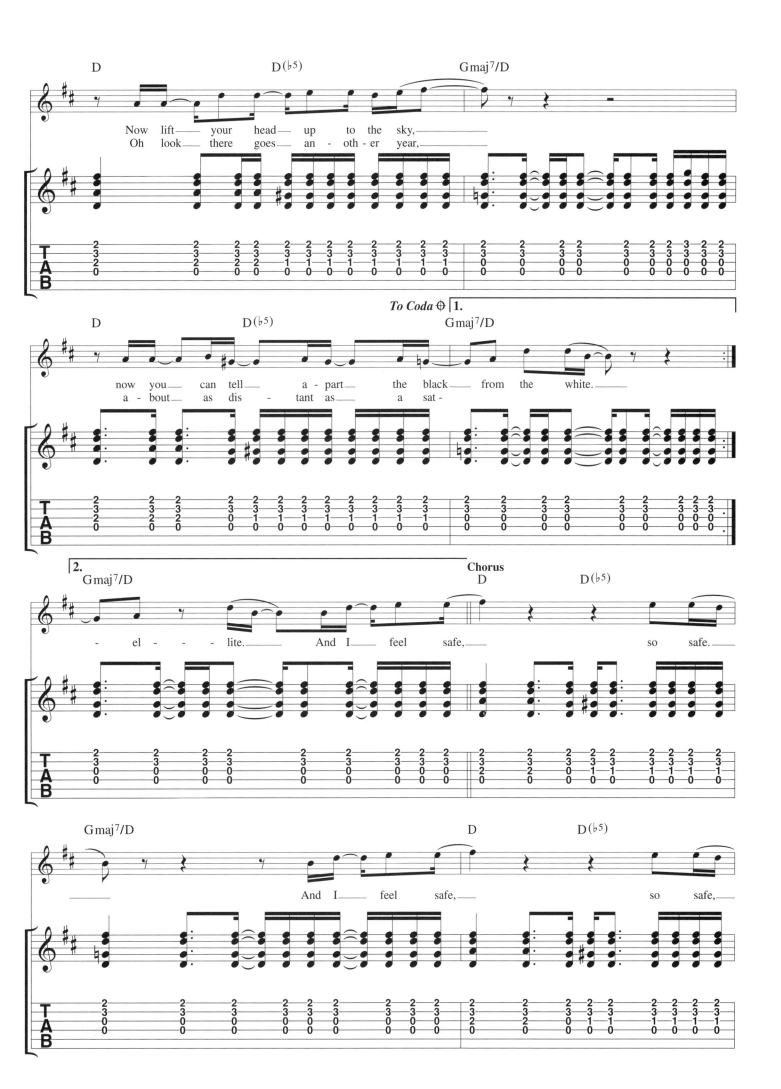

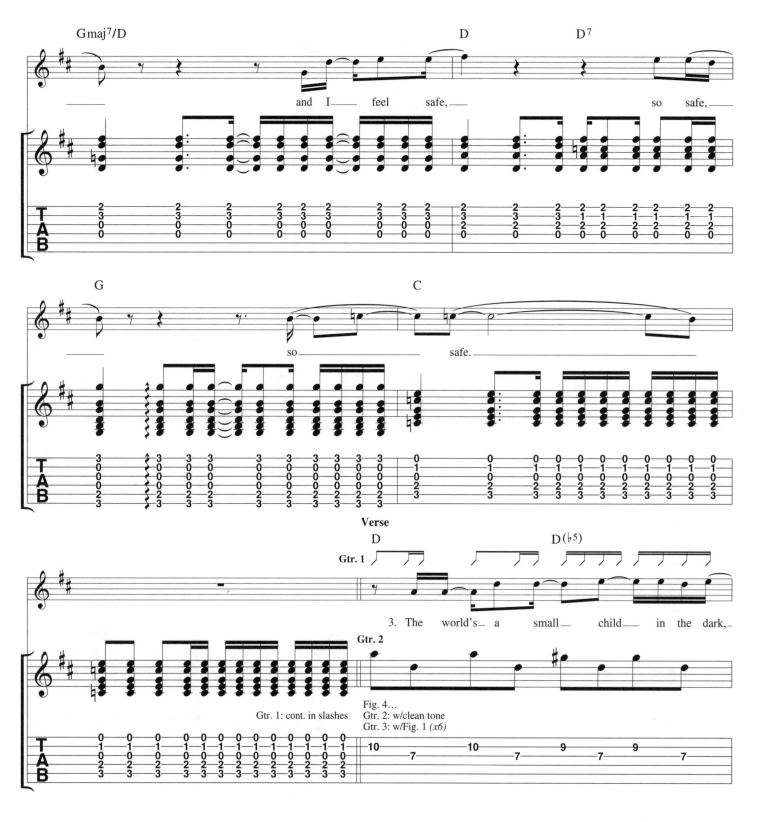

and I feel safe, so safe, so safe.

Verse

Gtr. 1

3. The world's a small child in the dark,

Gtr. 2

Fig. 4...
Gtr. 1: cont. in slashes
Gtr. 2: w/clean tone
Gtr. 3: w/Fig. 1 *(x6)*

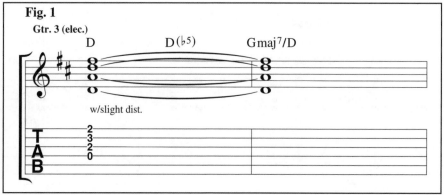

Fig. 1

Gtr. 3 (elec.)

w/slight dist.

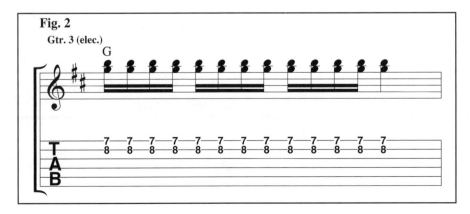

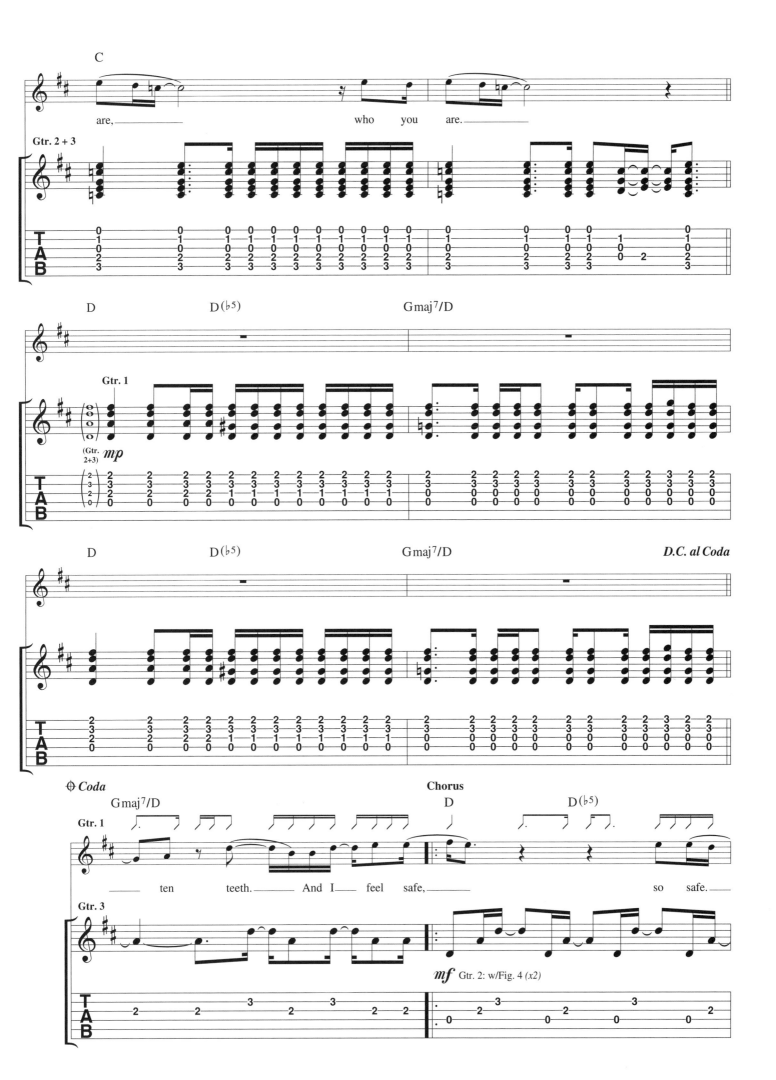

Gmaj7/D ..... D ..... D(b5)

cont. sim.

And I feel safe, so safe.

Gmaj7/D ..... D D7

And I feel safe, so safe,

Gtr. 2 w/Fig. 5

G ..... C ..... 1.

so safe. And I feel safe,

Gtr. 2 + 3

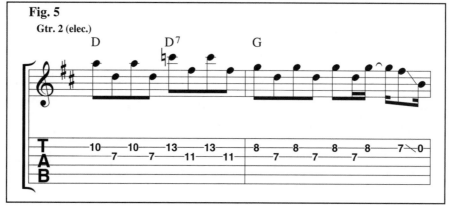

Fig. 5

Gtr. 2 (elec.)

D ..... D7 ..... G

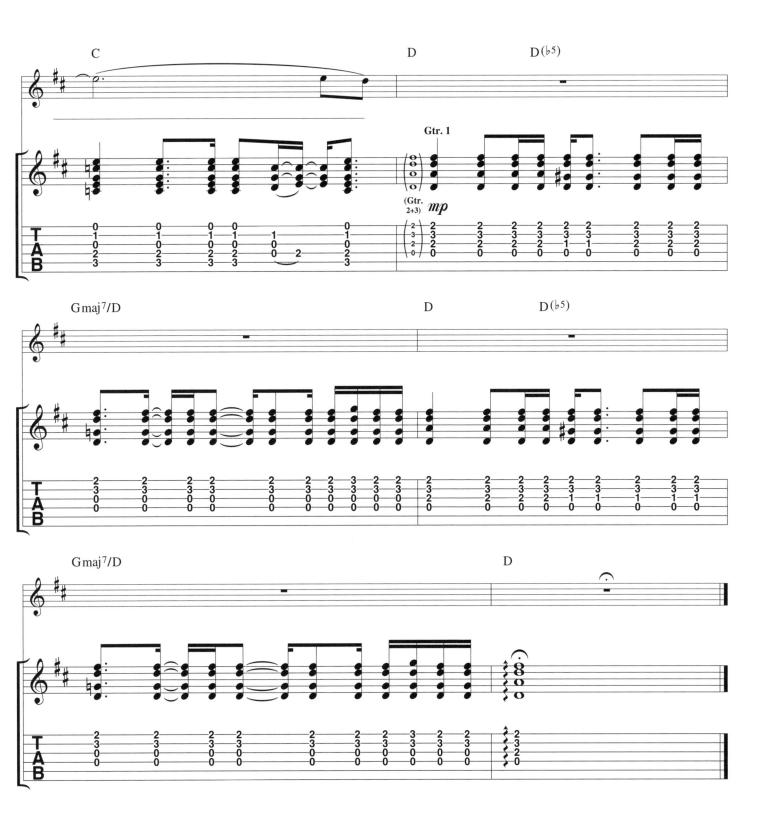

Verse 3:
When I was young things didn't last
My only care stemmed to the price of sweets
Now I am older I can laugh
A dolly mixed up man with rotten teeth.

And I feel safe *etc.*

Follow The Light

Words & Music by Fran Healy

Gtrs. 1+2: Capo 2nd fret
Gtrs. 3, 4+5: Standard tuning

*Symbols in parentheses represent chord names with respect to capoed guitar (TAB 0= 2nd fret).
Symbols above represent actual sounding chords.

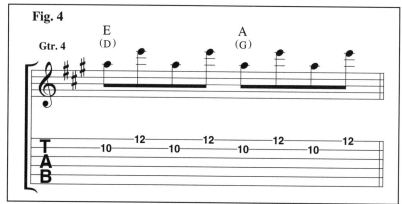

Fig. 4

Last Train

Words & Music by Fran Healy

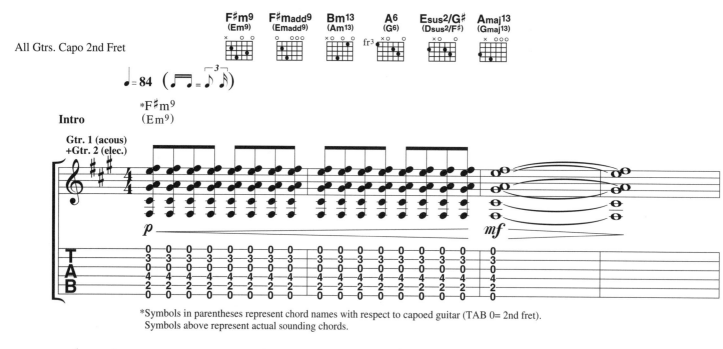

All Gtrs. Capo 2nd Fret

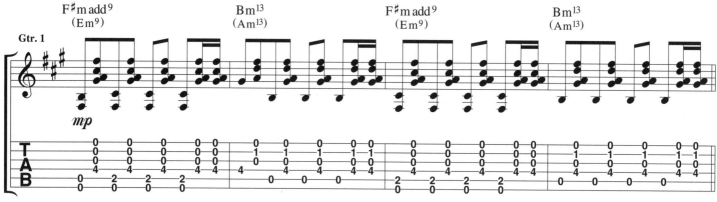

*Symbols in parentheses represent chord names with respect to capoed guitar (TAB 0= 2nd fret).
Symbols above represent actual sounding chords.

1. Rain on the brain,___ and now there's flow - ers in your win -
within your - self,___ for feel - ing, ev - 'ry - bo - dy's got

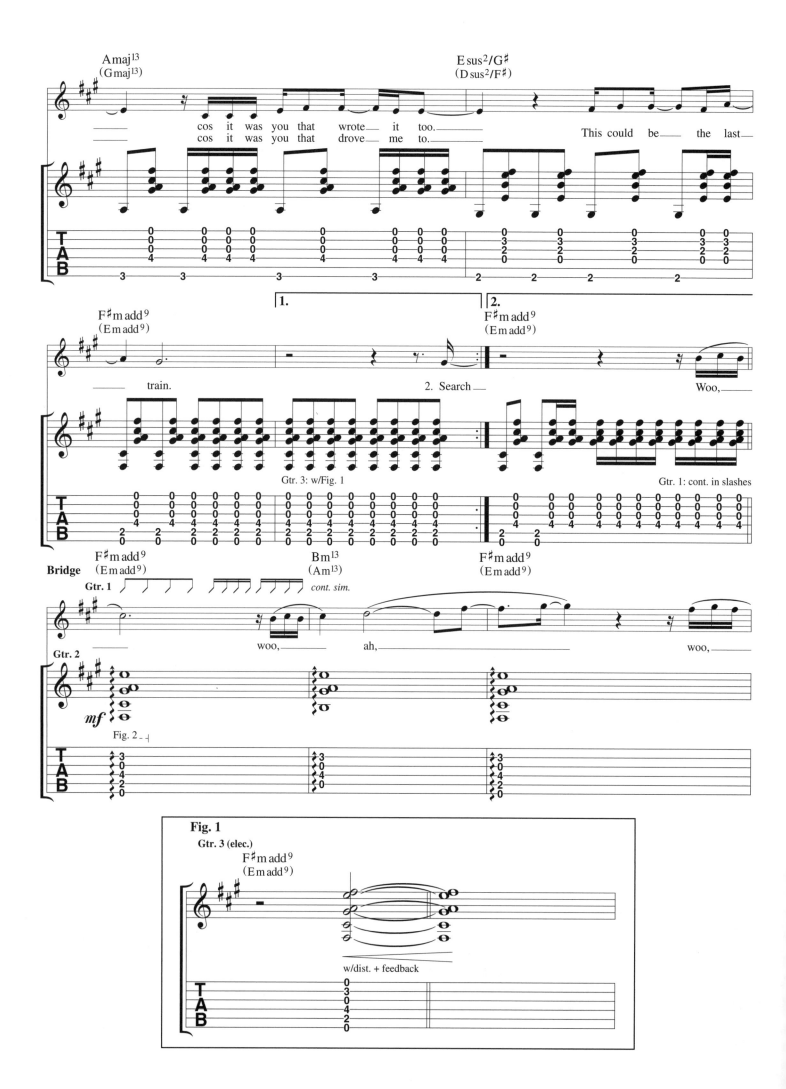

Afterglow

Words & Music by Fran Healy

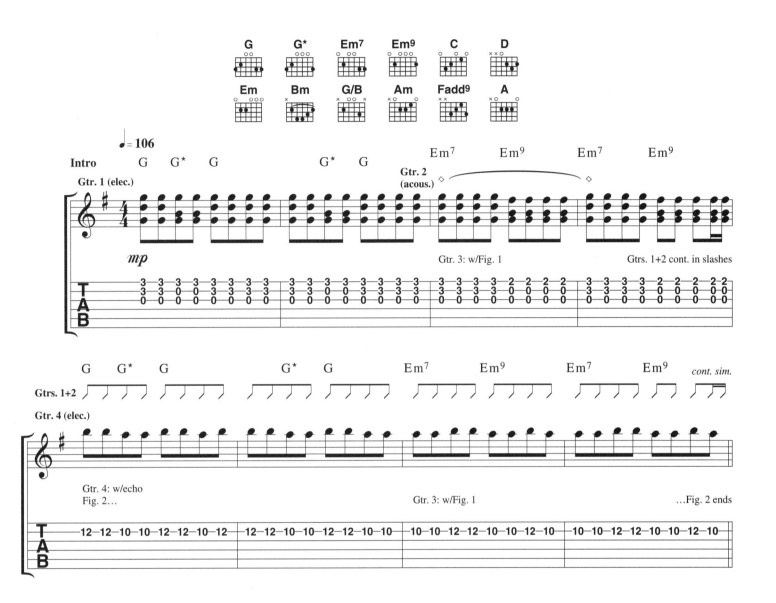

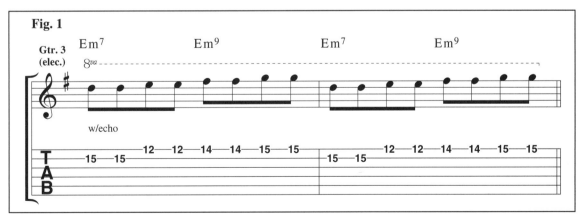

Fig. 1

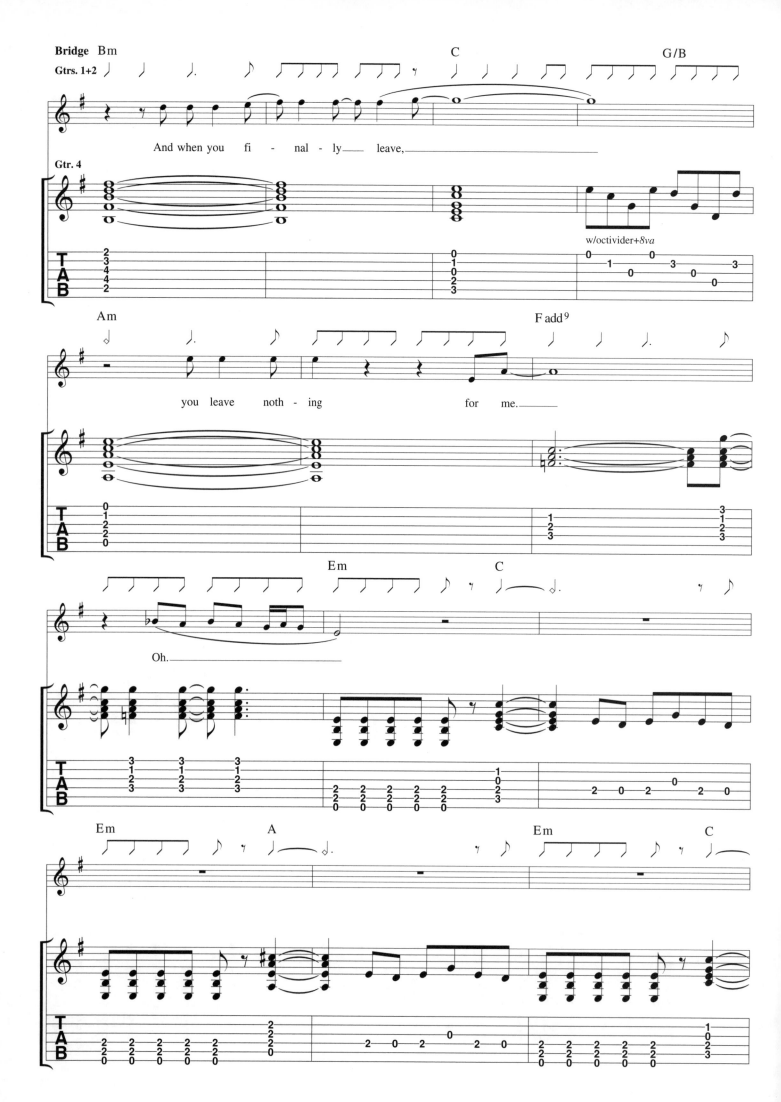

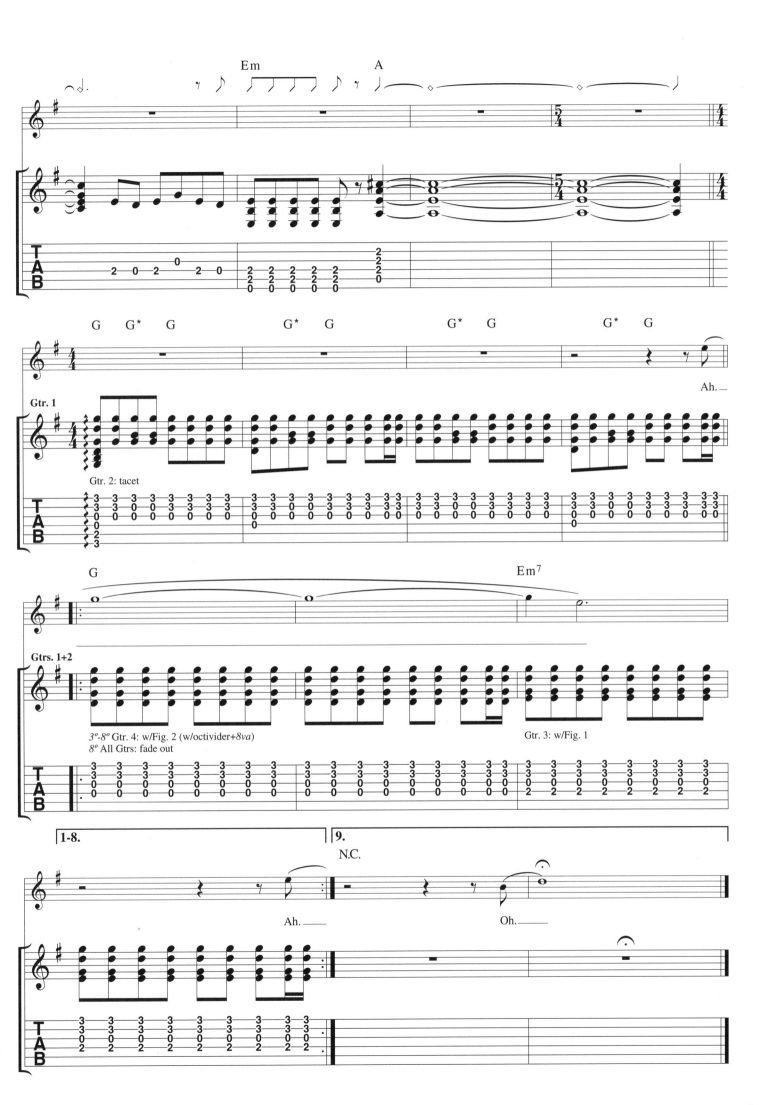

Indefinitely

Words & Music by Fran Healy

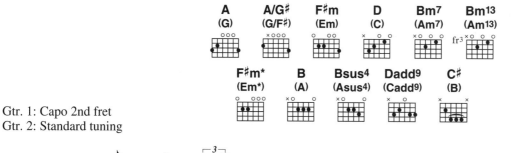

Gtr. 1: Capo 2nd fret
Gtr. 2: Standard tuning

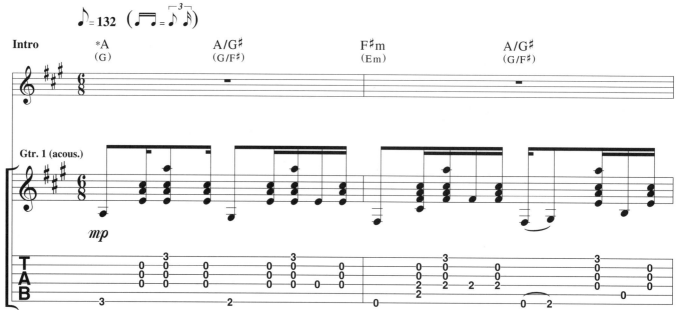

*Symbols in parentheses represent chord names with respect to capoed guitar (TAB 0= 2nd fret).
Symbols above represent actual sounding chords.

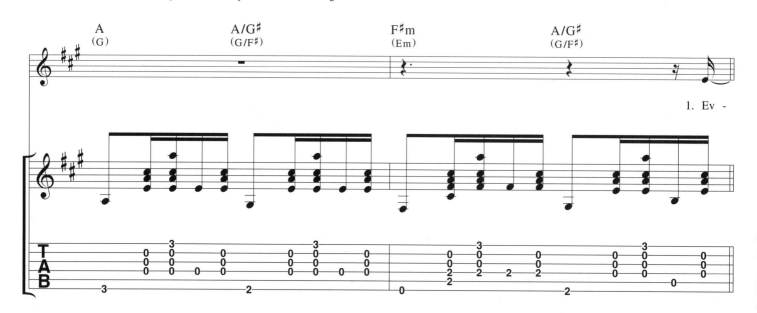

1. Ev -

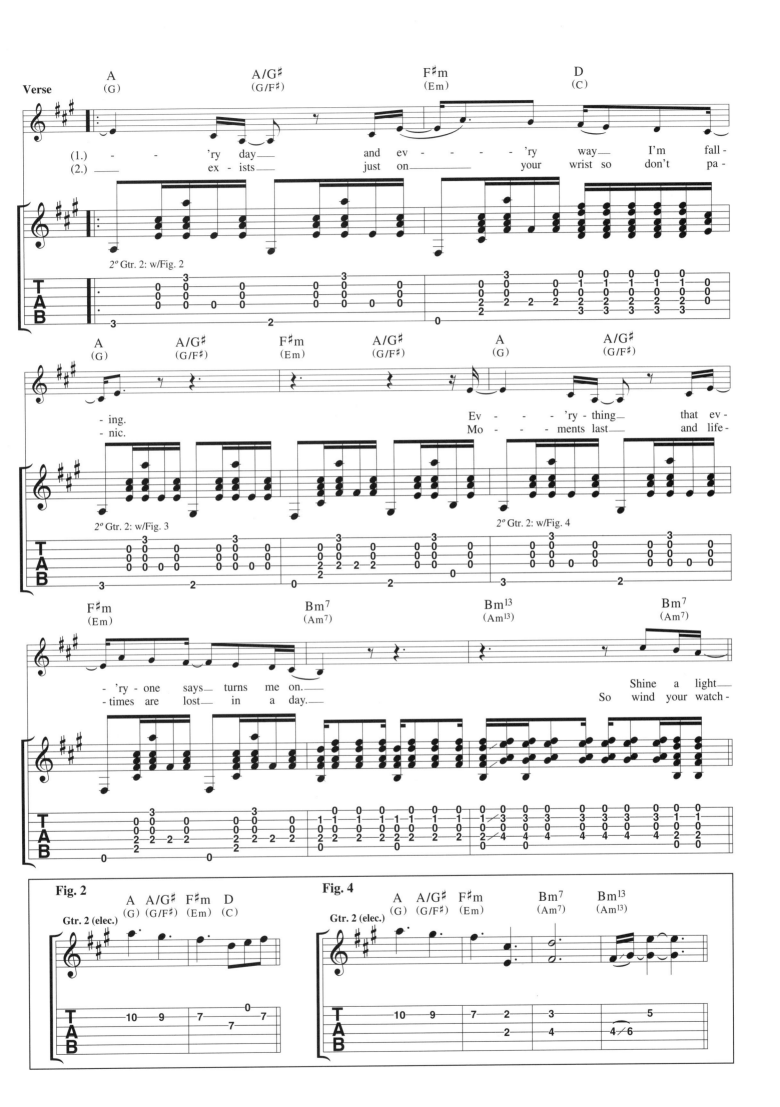

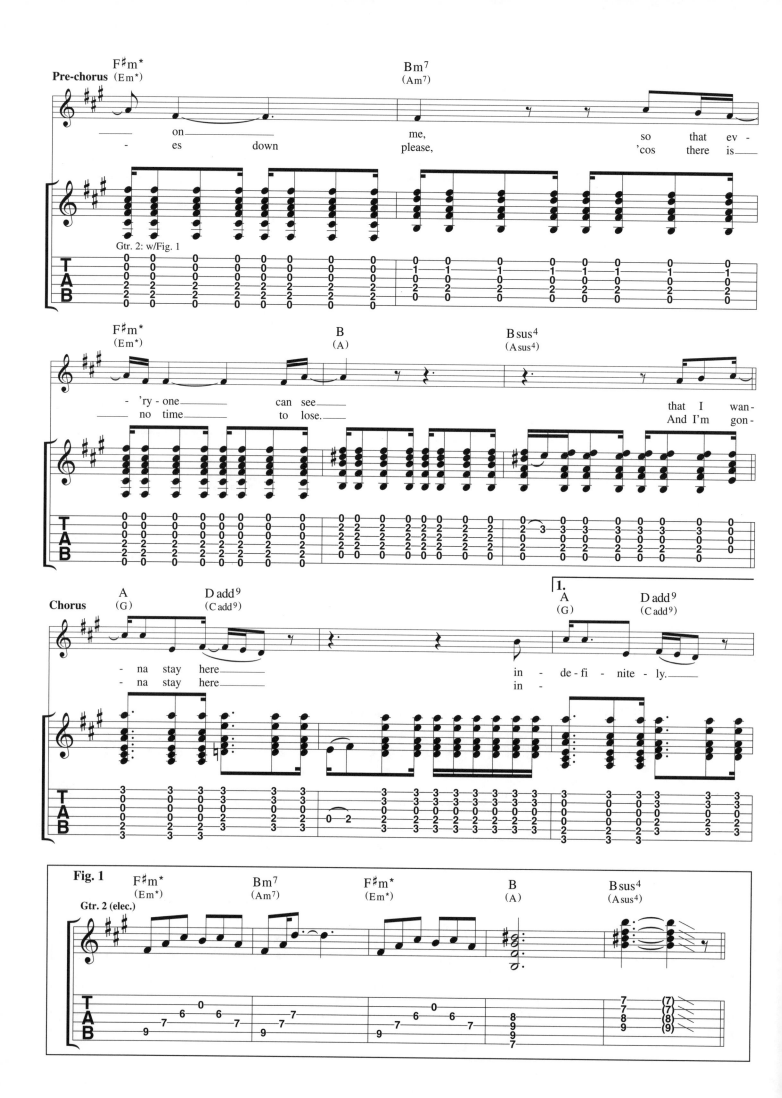

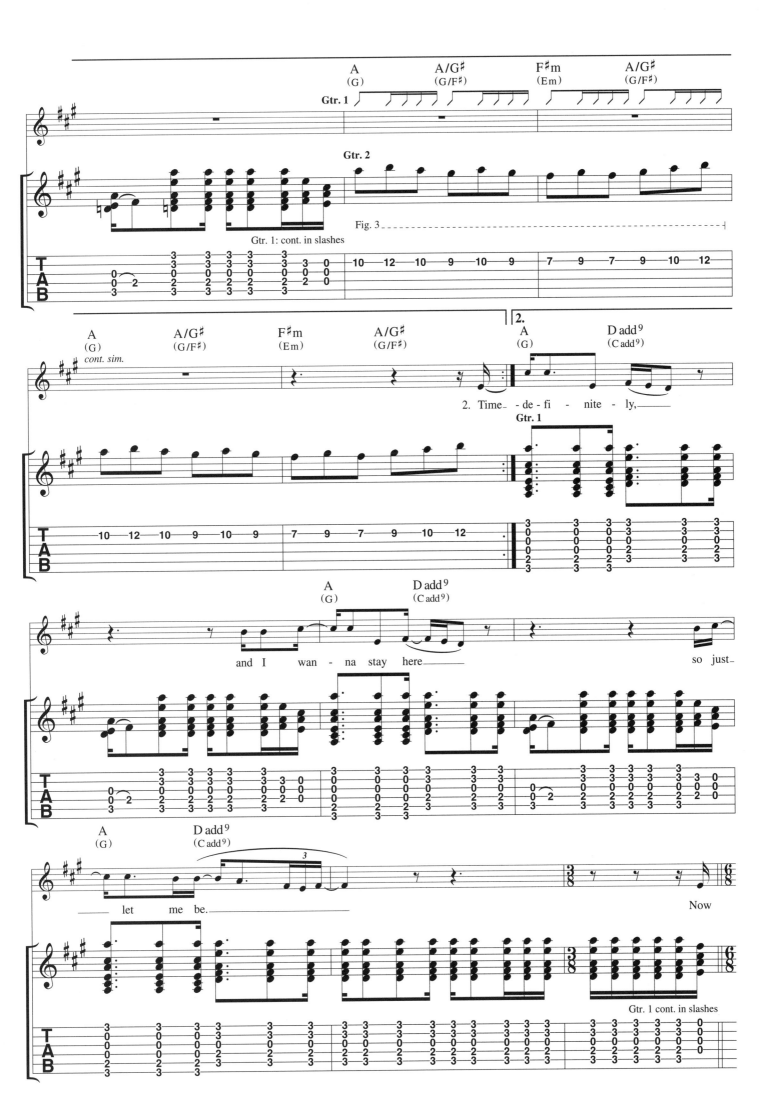

The Humpty Dumpty Love Song

Words & Music by Fran Healy

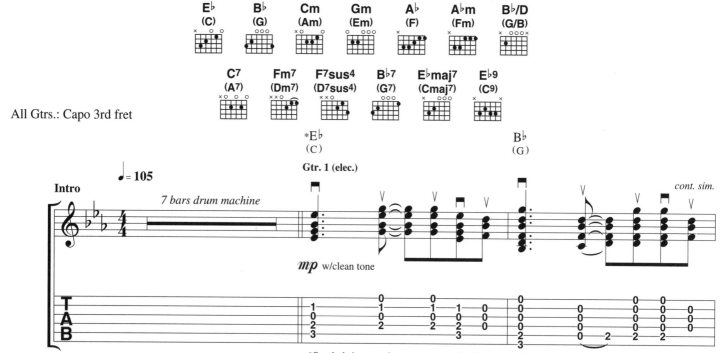

All Gtrs.: Capo 3rd fret

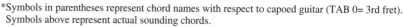

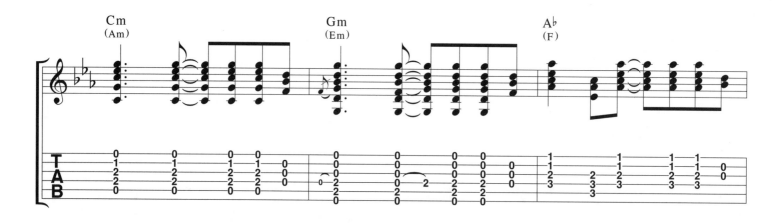

*Symbols in parentheses represent chord names with respect to capoed guitar (TAB 0= 3rd fret).
Symbols above represent actual sounding chords.

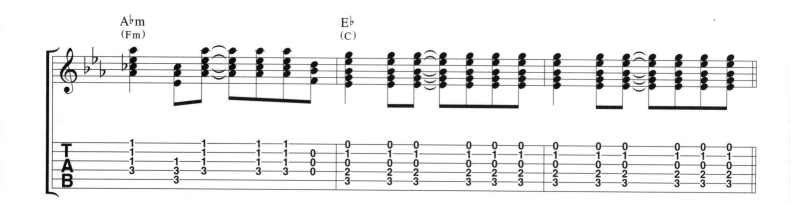

Verse

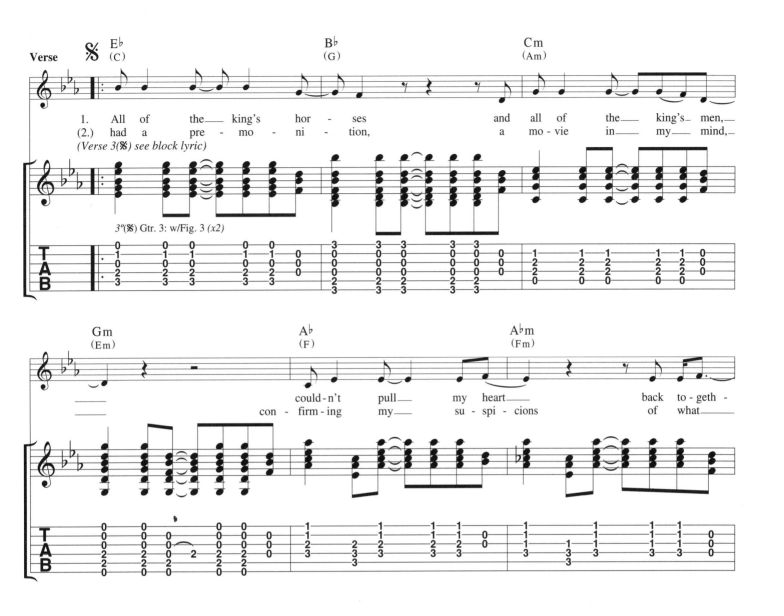

1. All of the king's hor - ses and all of the king's men,
(2.) had a pre - mo - ni - tion, a mo - vie in my mind,
(Verse 3(%) see block lyric)

3º(%) Gtr. 3: w/Fig. 3 *(x2)*

could - n't pull my heart back to - geth -
con - firm - ing my su - spi - cions of what

Fig. 3

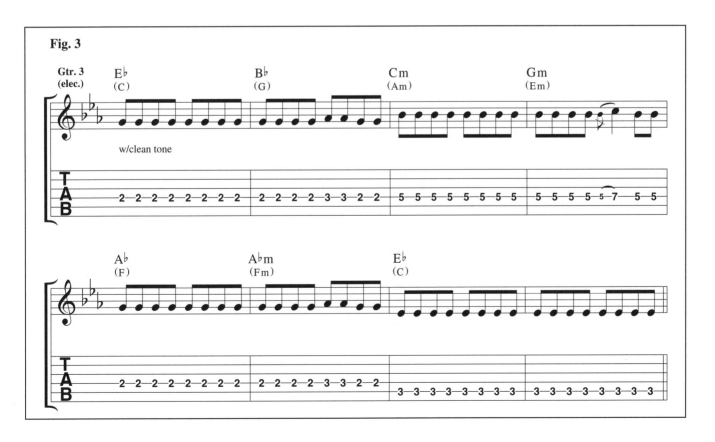

w/clean tone

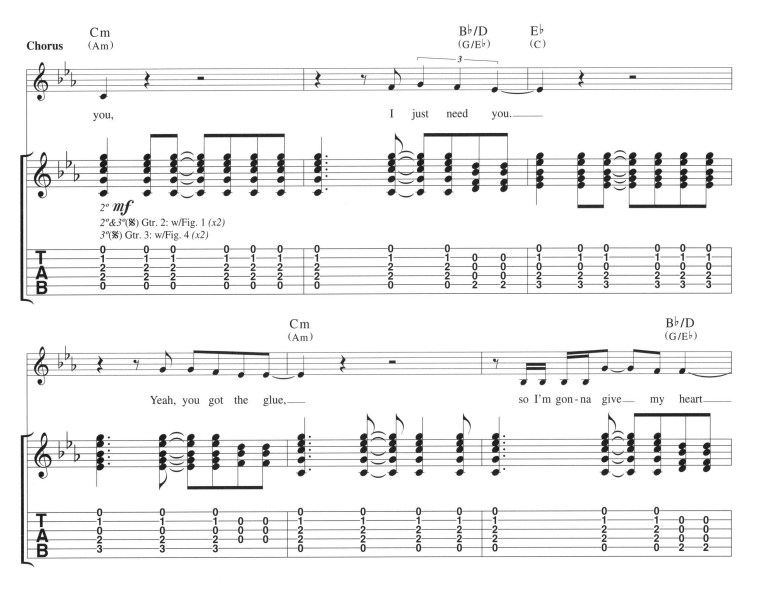

Chorus

you,   I just need you.——

2° *mf*
2°&3°(𝄋) Gtr. 2: w/Fig. 1 *(x2)*
3°(𝄋) Gtr. 3: w/Fig. 4 *(x2)*

Yeah, you got the glue,——   so I'm gon-na give—— my heart——

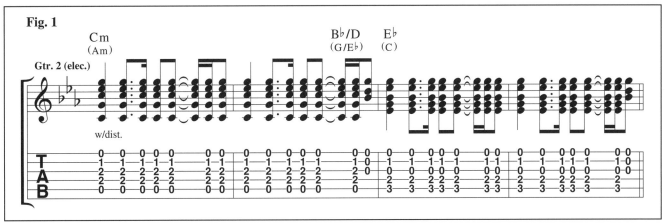

Fig. 1

Gtr. 2 (elec.)

w/dist.

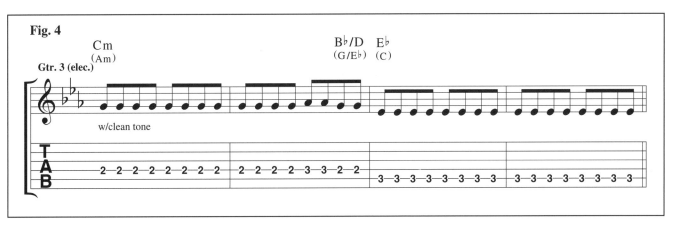

Fig. 4

Gtr. 3 (elec.)

w/clean tone

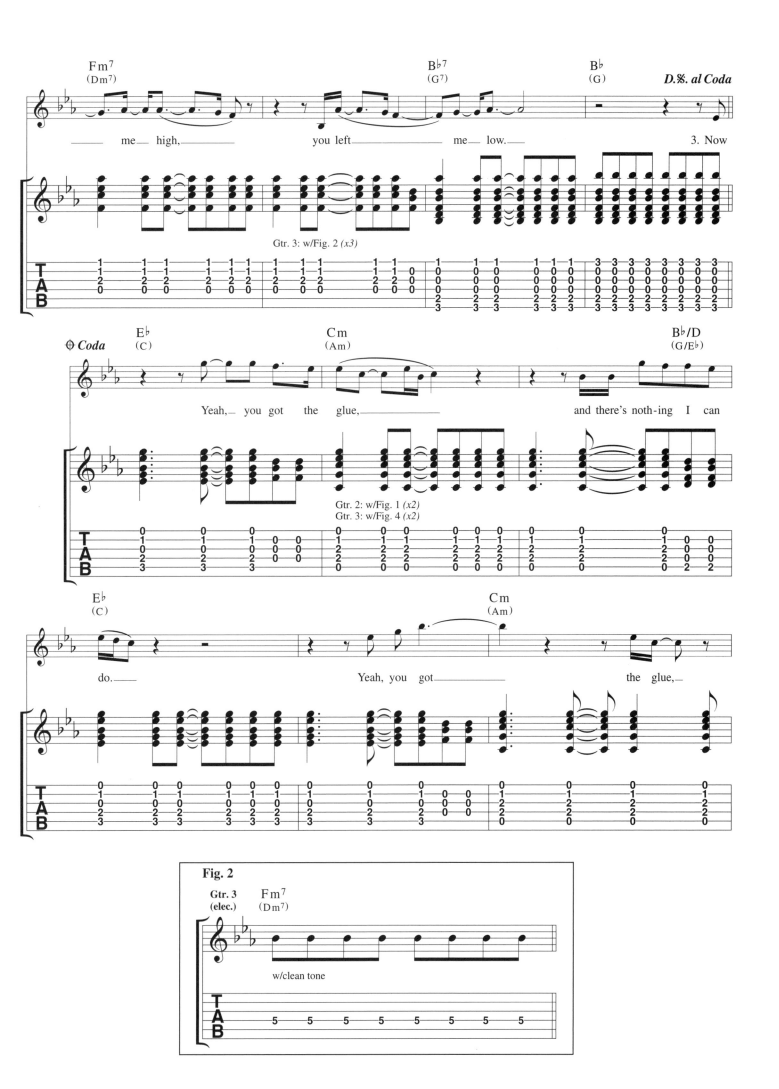

Verse 3:
Now as I lie in pieces and wait for your return
The sun upon my forehead burns, baby burns
An eye on all my horses, you've slept with all my men
I'm never gonna get it together again.

Still all I need is you *etc.*